FREDERICK WARNE
Published by the Penguin Group
Penguin Books Ltd, 27 Wrights Lane, London W8 5TZ, England
Penguin Putnam Inc., 375 Hudson Street, New York, NY 10014, USA
Penguin Books Australia Ltd, Ringwood, Victoria, Australia
Penguin Books Canada Ltd, 10 Alcorn Avenue, Toronto, Ontario, Canada M4V
3B2
Penguin Books (N.Z.) Ltd, 182-190 Wairau Road, Auckland 10, New Zealand

Penguin Books Ltd, Registered Offices: Harmondsworth, Middlesex, England

First published in 1999

5 7 9 10 8 6 4

ISBN 0 7232 4536 3

Printed in China by Imago Publishing Ltd.

THE
FLOWER
FAIRIES
BIRTHDAY BOOK

THE
ℱLOWER
ℱAIRIES
BIRTHDAY BOOK

CICELY MARY BARKER

January

January 1

January 2

January 3

January 4

January 5

Rhea rengado

January 6

January

January 7

January 8

January 9

Chiara Quain

January 10

January 11

January 12

The Box Tree Fairy

Tiny buds, the Winter through,
Wait to open in the Spring
In a scented yellow ring.

January

January 13

January 14

杜实

January 15

January 16

January 17

January 18

January

January 19

January 20

January 21

January 22

惠思佳

January 23

戴柠瑟

January 24

李莫言

The Pine Tree Fairy

January 25

January

January 26

January 27

January 28

January 29

Hailey chan

January 30

January 31

February

February 1

February 2

Han Qi Zhai

February

February 3

February 4

February 5

February 6

王丹阳

February 7

February 8

February

February 9

February 10

February 11

February 12

Angel James

February 13

February 14

The Snowdrop Fairy

Wait! the world shall waken;
It is not dead, for lo,
The Fair Maids of February
Stand in the snow!

February

February 15

Cindy Chen , 朱礼篇, 王泽玮

February 16

February 17

February 18

February 19

February 20

February

February 21

February 22

Soyeon Kim

February 23

February

February 24

February 25

王子奕

February 26

February 27

February 28

February 29

The Windflower Fairy

The Winter's long sleeping,
Like night-time is done;
But day-stars are leaping
To welcome the sun.

March

March 1

Thy Nguyen

March 2

March 3

March 4

Alan Guan

March 5

March 6

March

March 7

March 8

March 9

Elsa Su

March 10

March 11

March 12

The Almond Blossom Fairy

March 13

March

March 14

March 15

张一

March 16

高静

March 17

March 18

朱静怡

March 19

March

March 20

March 21

陈星航

March 22

March 23

寇若怡

March 24

March 25

宋丙初

March

March 26

出 赵泽

March 27

March 28

March 29

March 30

March 31

April

April 1

April 2

April 3

April 4

April 5

April 6

The Pear Blossom Fairy

Sing, sing, sing, you blackbirds!
Sing, you beautiful thrush!
It's Spring, Spring, Spring; so sing, sing, sing
From dawn till the stars say; "hush".

April

April 7

April 8

April 9

谢天羽

April 10

王沛羊

April 11

April 12

April

April 13

April 14

April 15

April 16

April 17

April 18

The Greater Celandine Fairy

April 19

April 20

April

April 21

April 22

April 23

April 24

April 25

April 26

April

April 27

_____

_____

April 28

Mom
_____

_____

April 29

Brianna D'lessandso
_____

_____

April 30

_____

_____

The Laburnum Fairy

All Laburnum's
Yellow flowers
Hanging thick
In happy showers

May

May 13

May 14

Eva Xu

May 15

陈宏远

May 16

May 17

May 18

May

May 19

May 20

May 21

May 22

May 23

May 24

The Red Clover Fairy

May 25

May

May 26

May 27

May 28

May 29

May 30

May 31

June

June 1

June 2

June 3

June 4

June 5

June 6

幕琵

June

June 7

June 8

June 9

June 10

June 11

June 12

侯圭萌

June

June 13

_____

June 14

_____

June 15

_____

June 16

Lily Su
_____

June 17

_____

June 18

甜甜
_____

The Rose Fairy

Best and dearest flower that grows,
Perfect both to see and smell;
Words can never, never tell
Half the beauty of a rose...

June

June 19

June 20

June 21

June 22

郑红

June 23

June 24

Paul Johnson, courtney dunkley, Hanoah xu

June

June 25

_____

_____

June 26

_____

_____

June 27

_____

_____

June 28

_____

_____

June 29

_____

_____

June 30

_____

_____

July

July 1

July 2

July 3

July 4

July 5

July 6

The Cherry Tree Fairy

Cherries in garden and orchard,
Ripe and red in the sun;
And the merriest elf in the treetops
Is the fortunate Cherry-tree one!

July

July 7

July 8

July 9

July 10

July 11

July 12

我爱

July

July 13

July 14

July 15

July 16

July 17

July 18

The White Bindweed Fairy

July 19

July 20

July

July 21

July 22

July 23

陆,昊

July 24

佟雨昕

July 25

July 26

July

July 27

July 28

田田

July 29

July 30

July 31

August

August 1

August 2

August 3

August 4

August 5

August 6

August

August 7

August 8

August 9

August 10

August 11

August 12

The Phlox Fairy

August in the garden!
Now the cheerful Phlox
Makes one think of country-girls
Fresh in summer frocks.

August

August 13

August 14

August 15

August 16

August 17

August 18

August

August 19

August 20

August 21

August 22

佟月寒寒

August 23

August 24

The Chicory Fairy

August 25

August

August 26

August 27

August 28

August 29

Michael Jackson

August 30

August 31

September

September 1

September 2

September 3

September 4

September 5

September 6

September

September 7

September 8

Caeda page

September 9

September 10

Johnathen S.

September 11

September 12

September

September 13

September 14

September 15

September 16

Dad

September 17

September 18

The Rose Hip Fairy

Gay as a gipsy
All Autumn long,
Here on the hedge-top
This is my song.

September

September 19

Angela Liu

September 20

September 21

September 22

September 23

September 24

September

September 25

September 26

September 27

杨雨泽

September 28

September 29

September 30

October

October 1

October 2

October 3

October 4

October 5

October 6

The Michaelmas Daisy Fairy

I'm waiting here to welcome every guest;
And tell them it is Michaelmas,
and soon the leaves will fall,
But *I* think Autumn sunshine is the best!

October

October 7

October 8

October 9

October 10

李房坤，James Liu (吳宥均)

October 11

October 12

October

October 13

October 14

田蕾

October 15

October 16

October

October 17

October 18

October 19

October 20

October 21

October 22

张恐

The Beechnut Fairy

October

October 23

吴临风

October 24

October 25

October 26

October 27

October 28

赵若君 Mrs. Schroeder!!! ♡

October

October 29

October 30

October 31

王晓悦

November

November 1

Lining Dai

November 2

November 3

November 4

November 5

November 6

The Sloe Fairy

And now is Autumn here, and lo,
The Blackthorn bears the purple sloe!

November

November 7

杨瑞晨

November 8

November 9

November 10

November 11

November 12

November

November 13

November 14

雷博雯

November 15

November 16

November 17

李玥

November 18

The Burdock Fairy

November 19

November 20

November

November 21

November 22

November 23

November 24

November 25

November 26

November

November 27

November 28

November 29

November 30

Doris Chen

December

December 1

December 2

王轶凤, Selena Kim, Hama (沫沫)

December 3

December 4

December 5

金毅

December 6

December

December 7

庄浩岳

December 8

December 9

December 10

December 11

自感伐

December 12

The Holly Fairy

Of all the trees (O hush and hear!)
The holly bears the crown!

December

December 13

December 14

December 15

December 16

December 17

December 18

朱辰

December

December 19

_____

_____

December 20

杨子獣 _____

_____

December 21

黄房 _____

_____

December 22

_____

_____

December 23

_____

_____

December 24

_____

_____

The Christmas Tree Fairy

December 25

JESUS

December

December 26

December 27

December 28

December 29

December 30

December 31